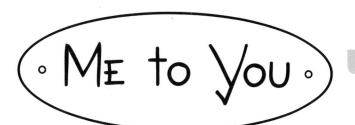

Me to You

Toys

Tatty Teddy x

Colouring Book

carte blanche
greetings ltd ®

www.alligatorbooks.co.uk

Published in 2013 by Alligator Books Limited
Gadd House, Arcadia Avenue, London N3 2JU
The Alligator logo is a registered trade mark of Alligator Books Limited.
Printed in Singapore 11779

Dear Santa

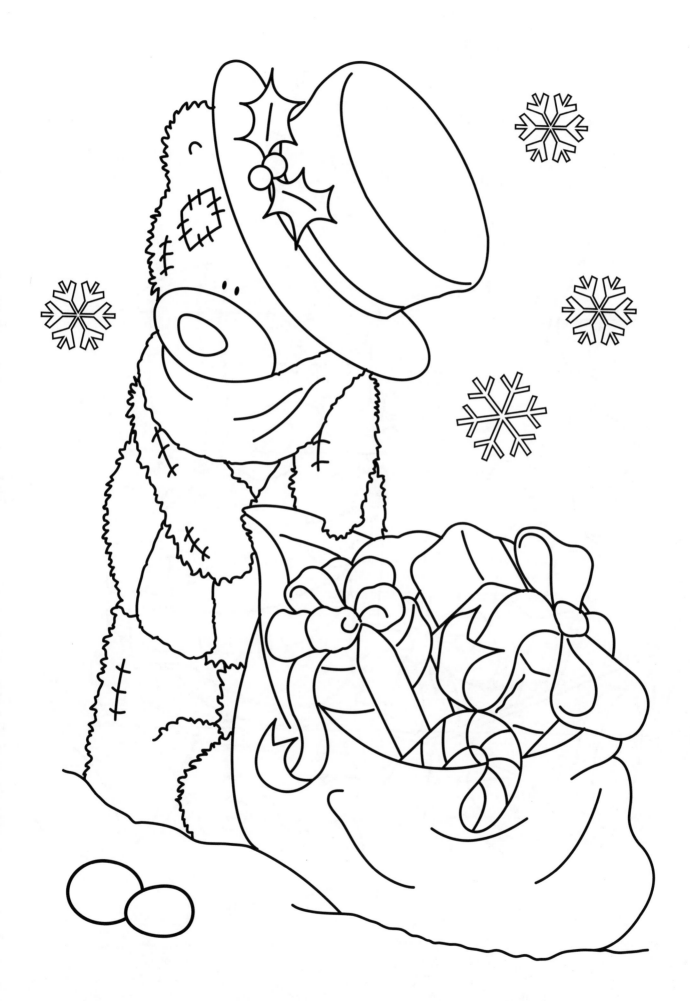

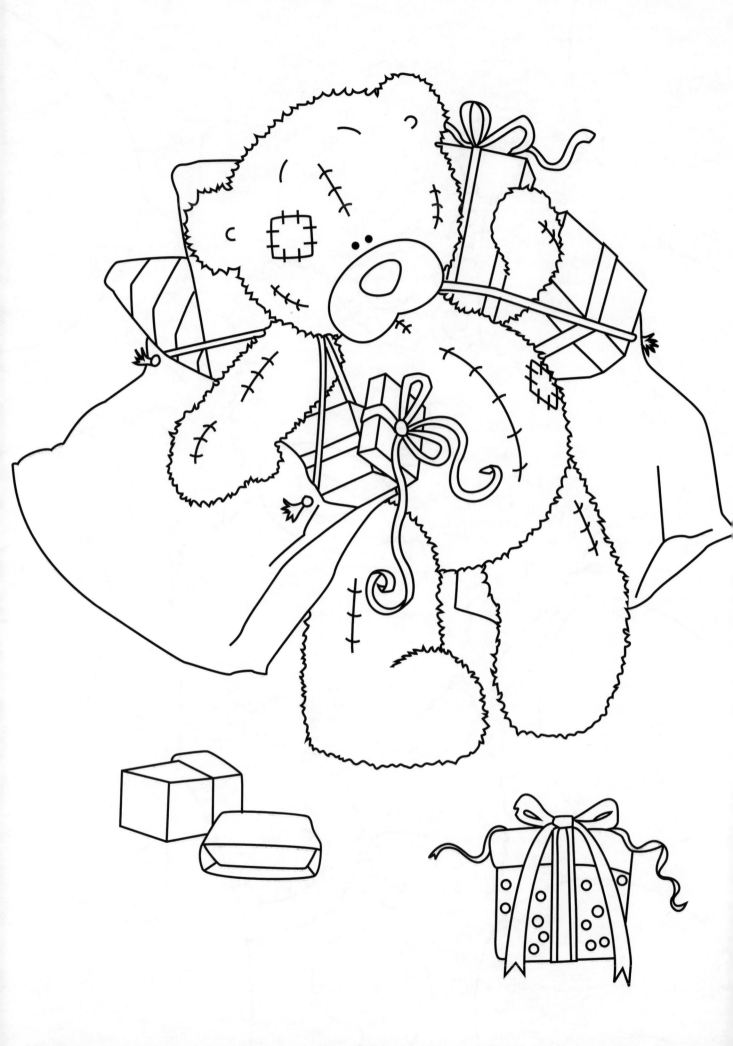

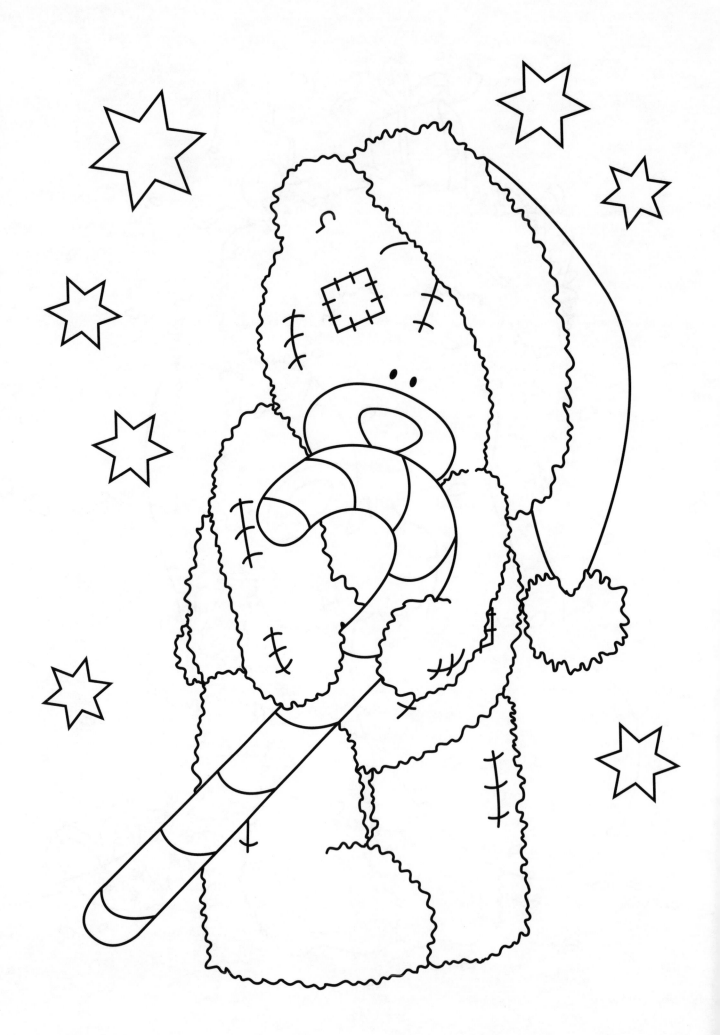

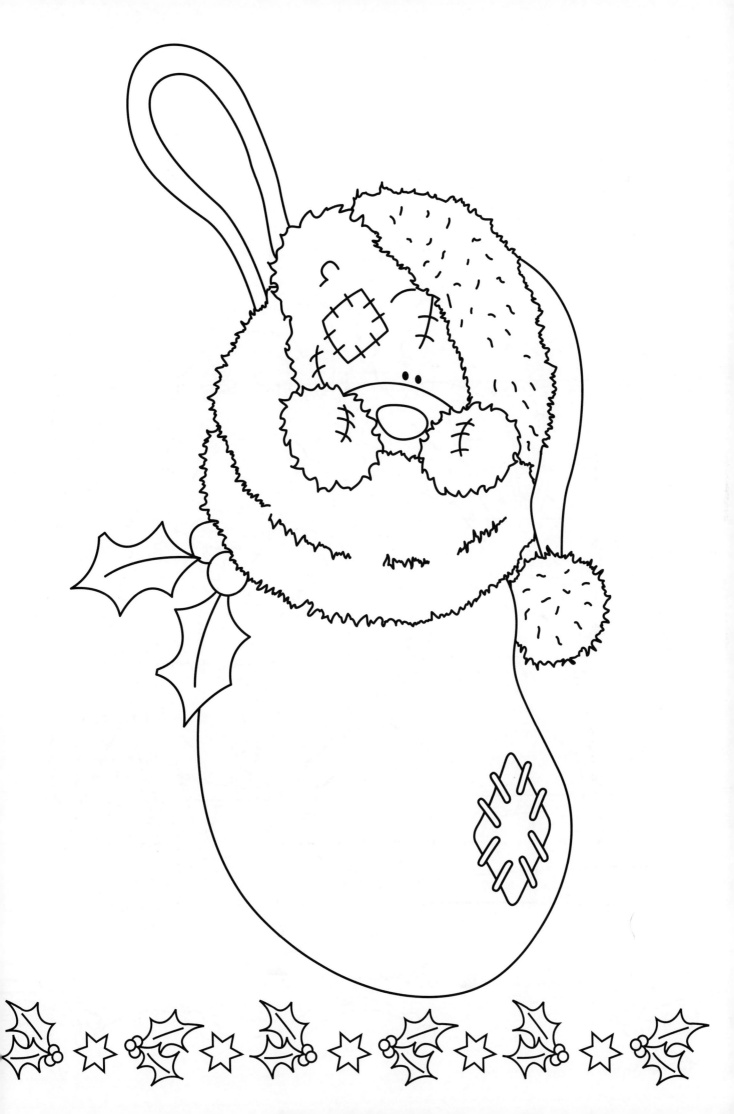

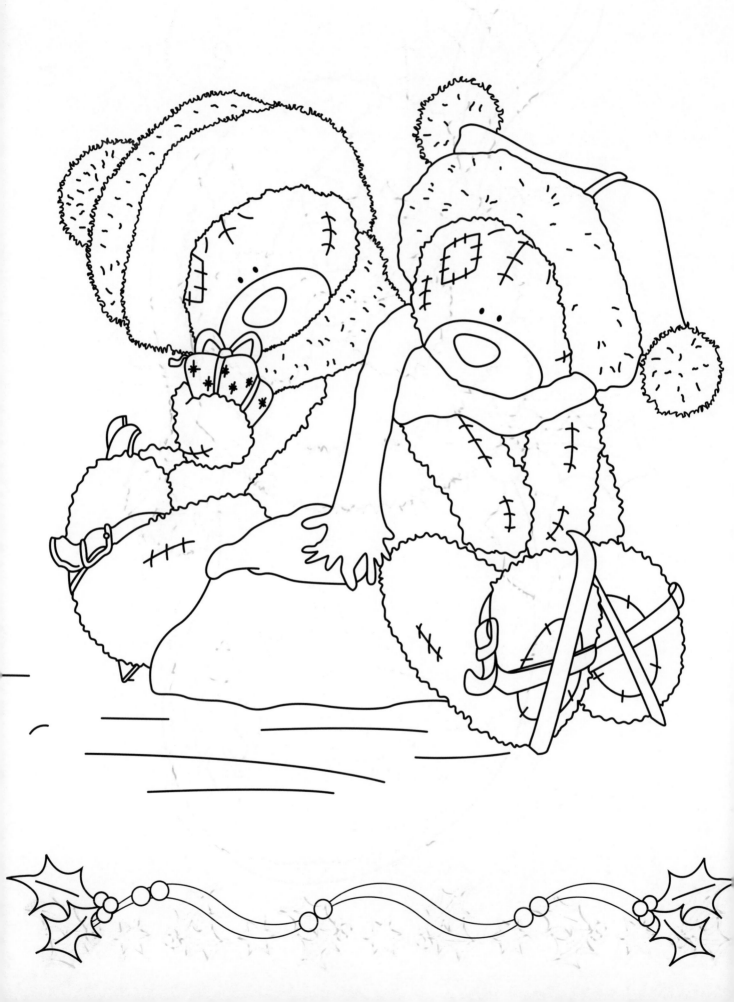

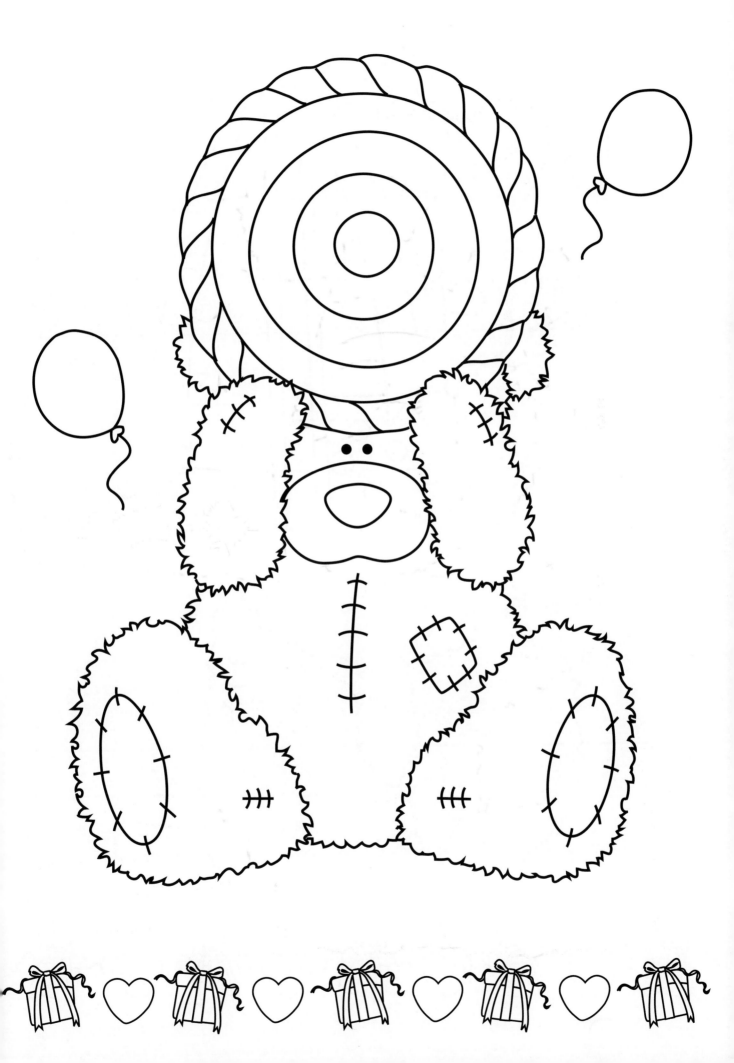

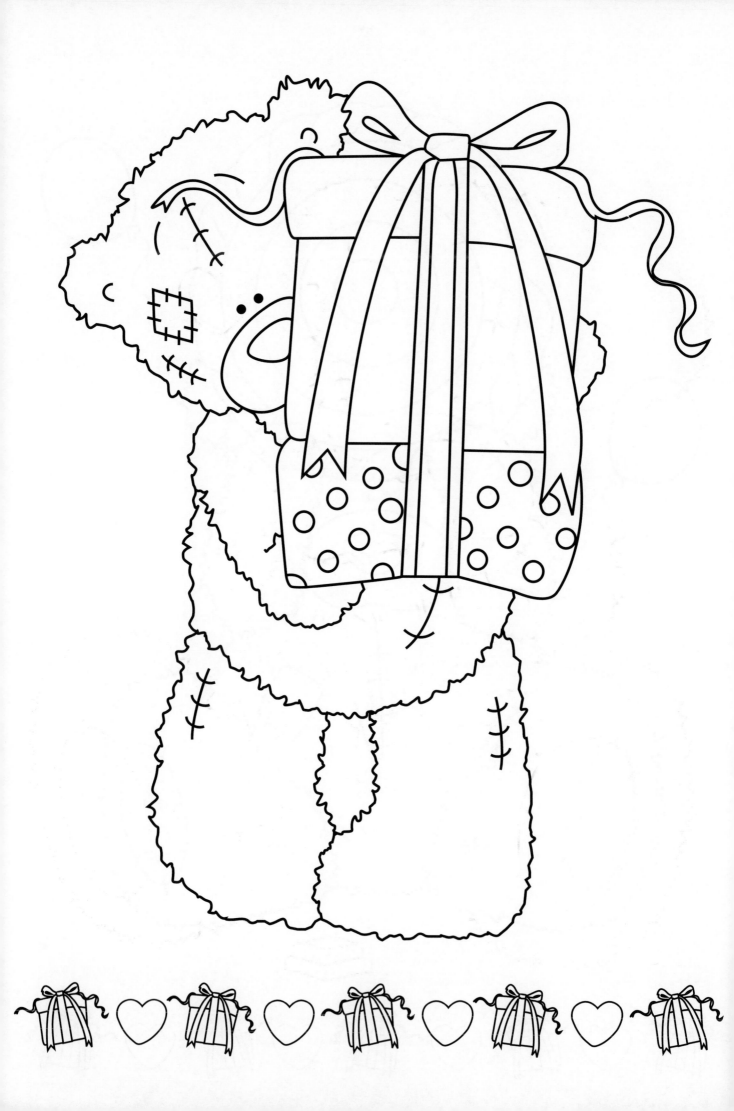

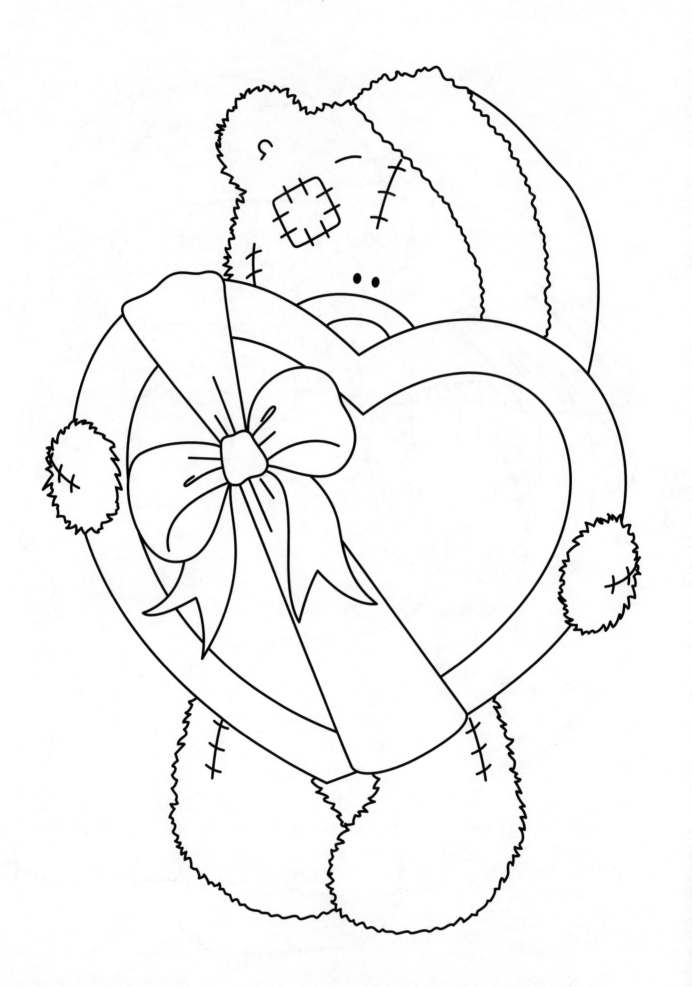

See you soon!